EMMY LOU®
By Marty Links

SBS SCHOLASTIC BOOK SERVICES
New York Toronto London Auckland Sydney

Copyright © 1971 by United Feature Syndicate, Inc. All
rights reserved. Published by Scholastic Book Services, a
division of Scholastic Magazines, Inc.

1st printing March 1971   Printed in the U.S.A.

"Devvie's father drives *her* to school when it rains, Merla's father drives *her*, Horty's father drives *her*, June's father drives *her*...."

"TV is really good for your health. It keeps you from concentrating too hard on homework and maybe getting a headache!"

"Something in old lavender for a woman getting on in years . . . It's my mother's birthday!"

"It's about time you called, Alvin. Life is certainly miserable around here if you don't call!"

"Imagine being asked to leave just because we gave him a standing ovation when he appeared on the screen!"

"Alvin said of course he doesn't mind if you come along with us! . . . You still got that $2.50 you had on you yesterday?"

"Let's save a seat between us. That cute usher just *might* get tired of standing up!"

"Alvin, sometimes I think you care more for
this car than you do for me!"

"Alvin may not be here, but he's certainly left his imprint on this family!"

"When Alvin asks for a hamburger, it's well done. When he asks for the check, it's rare!"

"We've used up all our money, sir. Could you
deliver us home C.O.D.?"

"I decided to give Raymond one more chance
—but he didn't take that one, either!"

"Well, we know one thing about Alvin! When it comes to money he's a conservationist!"

"I can just see that dress on you, Mom—but
first I can just see it on me!"

"It's an invitation to a costume party! I'll have to think of something really far-out to wear!"

"I'll say he's a life-saver! He asked me for a
date Saturday night!"

"I don't understand why my allowance goes lower with the stock market but never up with it!"

"These carefree days of summer would be okay—if they weren't so boy-free, too!"

"Stanleigh wants to know what we're having for dinner, but he says he'll stay anyway!"

"I'll buy you a maxi-coat when they come
down to a mini-price!"

"You know, Emmy Lou, I kinda liked <u>Hamlet</u>. Did Shakespeare write anything else?"

"I don't think I'm in favor of lowering the voting age. Alvin will become 21 soon enough!"

"I know it's homework—but does that mean
particularly *this* home?"

"You notice that since Alvin's become a regular customer here, they no longer leave the catsup and relish on the counter!"

"One good thing about having Alvin along on a picnic: There isn't much litter to clean up afterwards!"

"It seems to me that you and Alvin are ver[y] compatible — between fights!"

It must be serious. He's the only one Emmy
Lou sees during prime time!"

"One thing about Alvin—when it comes
homework, he's a conscientious objector!'

me day Emmy Lou will have her very own
dit card—and bankrupt the whole world!"

"Alvin's been gone two days now and I miss
him just as much as the day he left!"

"Dink met my parents last night and he still adores me!"

"Taffy, do you know who the *real* 'silent majority' is? All those boys out there who aren't asking us for dates!"

"Civil rights don't mean much around here!
I asked Daddy for a raise in my allowance
and he wasn't even civil to me!"

"Taffy, you might as well take it down—if it
hasn't worked by now!"

"...t know if this is such a good time to ...ke up with Alvin—just as his car breaks down!"

"Inviting Alvin for dinner is okay,
wanting to know first what's on the m...
is not!"

"But Alvin *does* take vitamin pills, Mom.
Matter of fact it's time he woke up to take
another one!"

"At least you're consistent, Alvin. Even your boat looks like a used car!"

"Taffy, do you realize what we're actually doing is taking care of someone who'll grow up and give us competition?"

"I need some extra money, Daddy. Do you have any chores—like cleaning my room?"

"Now, *there* is the forest's prime evil!"

"Okay, Taffy, I'll meet you half way—both
of us will give him up!"

"It's Alvin at the age of 10 months. It's the
only good picture he has of himself!"

"But, Taffy, maybe you can find a boy who wants to be a dentist and will *love* the bands on your teeth!"

"As a close friend, Sally possesses some beautiful qualities—such as a really cute older brother!"

"C'mon now, Daddy, don't be stingy! It's for
your birthday present!"

"Golly, my allowance doesn't go very far—
just about from the house to here!"

"The way she throws herself at boys is disgraceful, disgusting, and very practical!"

"Okay, Taffy, so tonight it's *your* turn to dream about Peter Fonda!"

"Breaking up with me is your privilege, Alvin, but I demand two weeks' notice!"

"Alvin says that lots of sleep is what keeps his mind so razor-sharp!"

"He's a brat, all right! Maybe they should have sent him, instead of the dog, to obedience school!"

"But a five-year age difference isn't bad, Taffy. When you're 85, he'll only be 90!"

"Start the hi-fi! Dim the lights! Here comes
my new date!"

"Yes, I do believe Emmy Lou has achieved
the 'total look'—total disaster!"

"There but for the grace of a terrific figure, naturally blonde hair, and her own car go I!"

"Emmy Lou and Alvin fight so much they ought to start a scrapbook!"

"Dante is sort of shy, Mom, so we have to
do our best to make him feel at home!"

"There goes a former girl friend of mine
with a former boyfriend of mine!"

"Car, looks, money! He's got everything he needs—except me!"

"Funny, Alvin, I never figured you as having wisdom teeth!"

"I'd like to buy my daughter some records for her birthday. Do you carry any of the old-fashioned breakable ones anymore?"

"One good thing about Emmy Lou getting married some day—we'll be losing a daughter but gaining a bathroom!"

"Golly, Alvin, you paint the way you think —abstract!"

"Why, it's full! Hasn't Alvin been here today?"

"Taffy's just practicing smiling. . . . She gets
the bands off her teeth tomorrow!"

"Alvin, I wish you'd try earning the money
for our dates a little more in advance!"

"I've never trusted these movie magazines since the time one said Peter Fonda liked only redheads!"

"Alvin was about to make up with me yesterday when Victoria walked by with two hamburgers!'

"Speaking of 'getting involved' — let's start with him!"

"Jean is on the perfect diet! She eats lunch
only when Jimmy pays for it!"

"He's everything Taffy ever dreamed of in a
boy—he's a boy!"

"I wish someone would organize an encounter group—starting with them!"

"Okay, Daddy, let's make a deal: I'll admit
I'm very spoiled if you'll let me have that new
bathing suit!"

"Alexander Graham Bell works a whole life-
time to invent the telephone just so you can
wait for a call from Alvin!"

"Ray Harold is a real gourmet! I told him what year I was born and he said that was a good year for girls!"

"Just think of the problems Tricia must have!
What boy would have the nerve to explain to
the President why he brought her home late?"

"It's certainly a relief to have been away from boys for the past three hours, 28 minutes, and seven seconds!"

"Well, yes, you could call Alvin's car a kind
of station wagon. It's always at the station
for repairs!"

"Do you have something that would make us look *less* natural?"

"Emmy Lou said she was expecting Barney
and Adele . . . Which one is it?"

"One thing about Alvin—he'll never get a
ticket for a moving violation!"

"Alvin is treating me to a dinner and a
movie.... Could I have some money?"

"When it comes to Alvin and me, I think it's more of a generation *gasp!*"

"I'm taking up a collection for a good cause—
me!"

"What are those French designers trying to
do to us now?"

"Let's go out a little too far again. I love to
hear him yell at us!"

"I was going to get Alvin a book as a birthday present, but he already has a book!"

"But, Daddy, I can't refuse to go to the movies with Alvin! He offered to pay!"

"I realize everybody is taking polls these days, but Alvin takes them on himself!"

"It's impossible to describe Alvin . . . You wouldn't believe it anyhow!"

"Let's see if I've got everything necessary for our hike—baby oil, mascara, eye liner, nail file . . . !"

"Of course I always obey my father! He tells me what to do and, if it sounds logical, I do it!"

"I can tell you why the Hollywood studios are in such financial trouble. Emmy Lou hasn't been going to any movies lately!"